KU-351-541

Magical Animals

It TRANSFORMS!

Magical Animals
That Change
Before Your Eyes

by Nikki Potts

raintree
a Capstone company — publishers for children

A+
books

Raintree is an imprint of Capstone Global Library
Limited, a company incorporated in England and Wales
having its registered office at 264 Banbury Road, Oxford,
OX2 7DY – Registered company number: 6695582

www.raintree.co.uk
myorders@raintree.co.uk

Edited by Jaclyn Jaycox
Designed by Ashlee Suker
Picture research by Tracy Cummins
Production by Tori Abraham
Originated by Capstone Global Library Ltd
Printed and bound in India

ISBN 978 1 4747 5162 9
21 20 19 18 17
10 9 8 7 6 5 4 3 2 1

British Library Cataloguing in Publication Data
A full catalogue record for this book is available from the
British Library.

Acknowledgements
We would like to thank the following for permission
to reproduce photographs: Alamy: blickwinkel/Trapp,
17; Science Source: D.P. Wilson/FLPA, 9, Francesco
Tomasinelli, 23, Stuart Wilson, 19; Shutterstock: Brandon
Alms, 6, Chuck Wagner, 25, Dirk Ercken, 4-5, 10, 22,
Jiri Prochazka, 20, Juan Sangiovanni, 16, kingfisher,
14, littlesam, 8, Mathisa, 2, 12, Matt Jeppson, 18,
MWermuth, 7, Narupon Nimpaiboon, 27, Paul Reeves
Photography, Back Cover, 15, StevenRussellSmithPhotos,
Cover, 24, Thanakorn Hongphan, 28, Tyler Fox, 29,
Vitalii Hulai, 26, Vladimir Sazonov, 13, xpixel, 21; Visuals
Unlimited: Michael Ready, 1, 11

We would like to thank Jody Rake of Southwest Marine
Educators Association for her invaluable help in the
preparation of this book.

CONTENTS

Did you know frogs begin life as tadpoles? And butterflies begin life as caterpillars? They go through a process called metamorphosis. There are two types of metamorphosis – complete and incomplete. Complete metamorphosis has four stages. Incomplete metamorphosis has three stages. All young animals grow and change. But when an animal goes through metamorphosis, it becomes something totally new!

BLACK SWALLOWTAIL BUTTERFLY

Black swallowtail butterflies are found in parts of North, Central and South America. A female lays an egg on a leaf or flower. A small caterpillar hatches four to nine days later. It eats leaves and grows. Soon its body hardens into a chrysalis. After a couple of weeks, an adult butterfly breaks out of the chrysalis. It is mostly black with orange, blue and yellow spots. Its wingspan can reach 8 to 10 centimetres (3 to 4 inches).

SEA SQUIRT

A sea squirt begins life as an egg. A tiny tadpole hatches from the egg. When the tadpole is ready, it attaches its head to the ocean floor or another surface. Soon the tadpole creates a protective layer around itself and transforms into a sea squirt! Colourful and see-through, an adult sea squirt's body has two short tubes. The tubes take in ocean water and filter food from it.

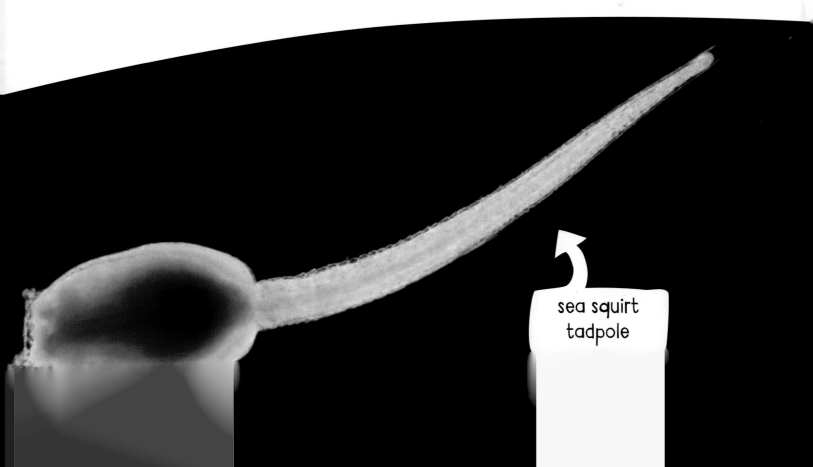

sea squirt
tadpole

PACMAN FROG

Pacman frogs are found in South American rainforests. An adult female frog lays eggs in water. Tadpoles hatch from the eggs. A tadpole has gills for breathing under water. Its back legs soon begin to grow. When the tadpole becomes an adult, it moves to land. Its gills disappear. The frog has a large mouth and tries to swallow anything that comes close. A pacman frog lives for six to seven years.

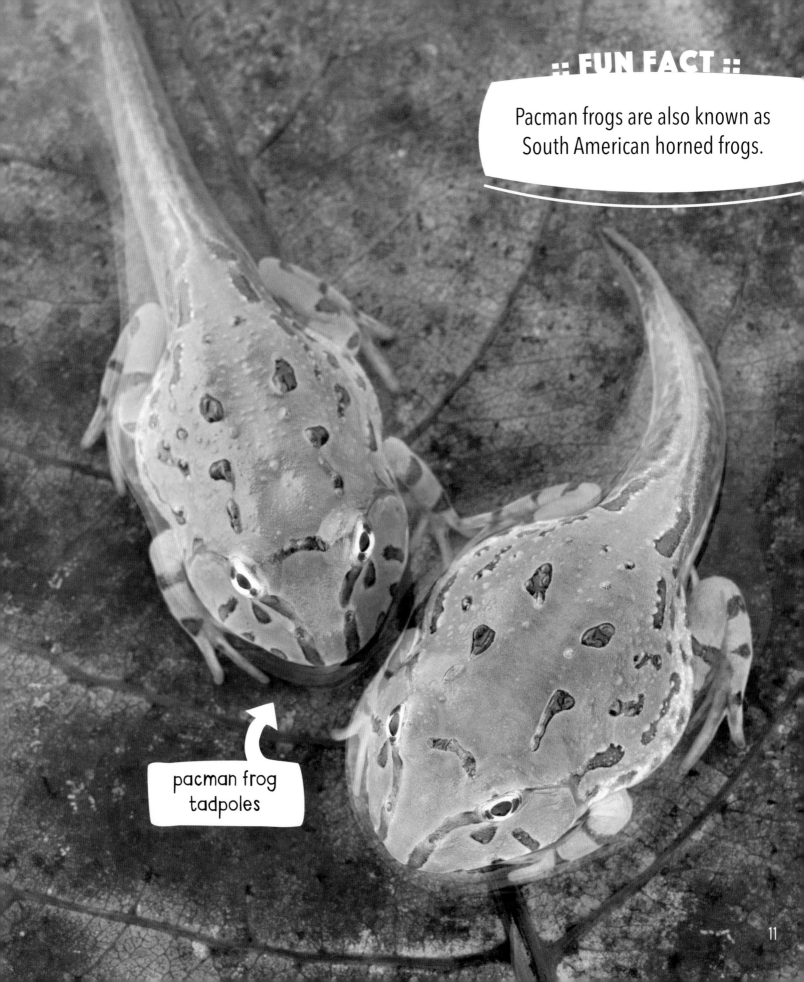

:: FUN FACT ::

Pacman frogs are also known as South American horned frogs.

pacman frog tadpoles

ATLAS MOTH

The atlas moth begins its life as a hungry caterpillar. It eats and eats for about 40 days before it builds a cocoon. Inside, the caterpillar turns into a pupa. After about one month, a large atlas moth breaks out of the cocoon. The moth's wingspan can stretch 27 centimetres (11 inches)! Atlas moths have no mouths, so they cannot eat. They live for only one to two weeks.

The atlas moth has the largest wing surface area of any moth in the world.

14

MONARCH BUTTERFLY

Look at those bright orange and black wings! It's a monarch butterfly. A monarch begins life as an egg. A tiny, green caterpillar hatches from the egg. The caterpillar grows and sheds its skin again and again. Finally, it attaches its body to a leaf. The caterpillar sheds its skin one last time. Then it forms a chrysalis around itself. Inside, the caterpillar changes into a pupa. After 9 to 15 days, a butterfly breaks free of the pupa. The monarch dries its wings and flies away.

:: FUN FACT ::

A monarch's bright colours warn predators to stay away. The milkweed it eats as a caterpillar makes it toxic to predators.

CANE TOAD

Large, poisonous cane toads have few predators. They are found in Australia, the southern United States and South America. Females lay 4,000 to 36,000 eggs at a time in water. Tadpoles hatch from the eggs. As a tadpole eats and grows, it slowly transforms into an adult. Its tail and body shrink, and legs begin to grow. Cane toads live for 5 to 10 years.

cane toad
tadpoles

:: FUN FACT ::

Most cane toads reach 10 to 15 centimetres
(4 to 6 inches) long. But the largest one
ever discovered was 38 centimetres
(15 inches) long. It weighed almost
3 kilograms (6 pounds)!

:: **FUN FACT** ::

Tiger salamanders dig deep burrows.
They have been found more than 61 centimetres
(24 inches) below ground. Burrowing helps
them to survive during hot or cold weather.

TIGER SALAMANDER

Tiger salamanders live in North America. They mate in shallow water. After mating, a female attaches eggs to a leaf, stem or twig. A larva hatches from an egg and lives in the water. The larva has a large head and gills. As it grows, it loses its gills. After a few weeks, the salamander reaches adulthood and gains its yellow spots or stripes. It moves from water and makes its home in a burrow on land.

tiger salamander larva

STAG BEETLE

Female stag beetles burrow deep underground to lay eggs. After a few weeks, white larvae hatch from the eggs. A larva sheds its skin many times. After about five years, it creates a cocoon out of soil. Inside the cocoon the larva becomes a pupa. Over the next five weeks, the pupa transforms into a beetle. When it breaks out of the cocoon, it darkens in colour and dries its wings. The beetle stays underground during winter. When summer comes, the beetle tunnels to the surface.

stag beetle larva

POISON DART FROG

Poison dart frogs are found in rainforests. Their bright colours tell predators to stay away. This frog's skin is poisonous. Females lay eggs on land. The males protect the eggs until tadpoles hatch. One parent will carry each tadpole to a bromeliad plant. The tadpoles eat algae and grow into froglets. They absorb their tails and grow legs. After about two months, the frogs jump out of the plant and onto the rainforest floor. Poison dart frogs live for three to five years.

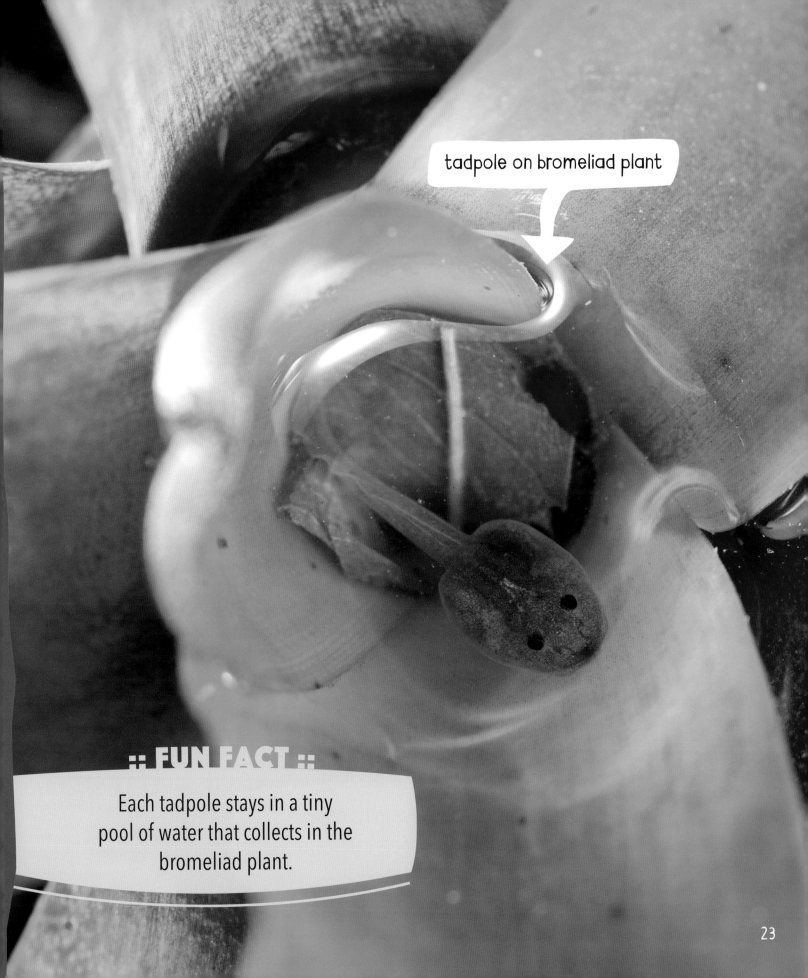

tadpole on bromeliad plant

:: FUN FACT ::

Each tadpole stays in a tiny pool of water that collects in the bromeliad plant.

An Io moth has large eyespots on its
hind wings. These eyespots can scare
away predators.

IO MOTH

Bright green Io moth caterpillars are found mostly in central and western North America. An Io moth begins life as a small white egg. A reddish larva emerges from the egg. The larva turns yellow and then green. It eats and eats for about four weeks. Then it creates a cocoon among the leaves. Inside, the larva becomes a dark brown pupa. An adult moth breaks out of the cocoon and stretches its wings.

DRAGONFLY

Dragonflies go through incomplete metamorphosis. They begin life in water as eggs. Nymphs hatch from the eggs and live under water. A dragonfly can live in the nymph stage for up to four years! When a nymph is fullly grown, it climbs up a plant stem. There it will shed its skin and become a dragonfly. The dragonfly has six legs and four wings. It has a long body and giant eyes. A dragonfly usually lives for only a few weeks as an adult.

dragonfly nymph

GRASSHOPPER

There are over 10,000 species of grasshopper. Grasshoppers also go through incomplete metamorphosis. Females lay eggs under sand, soil or leaves. Nymphs hatch from the eggs in spring. They look like adults but have no wings. After five to six weeks, a nymph becomes an adult. The grasshopper uses its long legs to leap away in search of food. Grasshoppers are found everywhere except Antarctica.

:: **FUN FACT** ::

Male grasshoppers can vibrate their wings to make noise and attract mates.

grasshopper nymph

GLOSSARY

ALGAE small plant-like living things that live in the sea and fresh water

BURROW hole in the ground made or used by an animal; also, to dig

CHRYSALIS hard shell inside which a pupa changes into a butterfly

COCOON covering made of silky threads; a moth makes a cocoon to protect itself while it changes from larva to pupa

FILTER remove unwanted materials

GILL body part on the side of an animal used to breathe

HATCH break out of an egg

LARVA animal at the stage of development between an egg and an adult

MATE join together to produce young; a mate is also the male or female partner of a pair of animals

METAMORPHOSIS changing from one form into a very different form, such as from a caterpillar to a butterfly

NYMPH young insect; nymphs change into adults by shedding their skin many times

POISON substance that can kill or harm someone

PUPA hard casing with an animal inside; the animal is changing from larval stage to the final animal stage

TRANSFORM change from one form to another

BOOKS

Adaptation and Survival (Life Science Stories),
Louise and Richard Spilsbury (Raintree, 2017)

Amazing Animal Shape-Shifters (Animal Scientists),
Leon Gray (Raintree, 2016)

RSPB First Book of Butterflies and Moths, Derek Niemann
(A&C Black Childrens & Educational, 2012)

WEBSITES

www.bbc.co.uk/nature/life/Lepidoptera
Discover more about the life cycle of butterflies and moths.

www.dkfindout.com/uk/animals-and-nature/amphibians/life-cycle-frog/
Follow the life cycle of a frog from frog spawn to adult frog.

Comprehension QUESTIONS

1. The black swallowtail butterfly and monarch butterfly form a chrysalis when going through metamorphosis. What is a chrysalis? Hint: Use the glossary for help!

2. Which two animals in this book go through incomplete metamorphosis?

3. Which animal in this book is your favourite? Why?

::INDEX::